TOP DOGS!

Written by C.J. McDonald
Designed by Flora Chan

10 9 8 7 6 5 4 3
ISBN: 978-1-338-76107-8
Printed in Jiaxing, China
Necklace made in Yiwu, China
5101856 05/23
Photos ©: 9 left: GlobalP/Getty Images; 13 bottom left: The Color Archives/Alamy Stock Photo; 44 center: Kurt Pas/Getty Images; 61 right: Jim Zuckerman/Alamy Stock Photo. All other photos © Shutterstock.com.

Acknowledgments

The author wishes to thank her border collie-mixes, Pepper and Biscuit, for their love, support, and inspiration throughout the writing of this book.

Table of Contents

A Friendship in Dog Years....4
Achieving Pupfection....5
Meet the Sporting Dogs....6
Top Dog: Labrador Retriever....7
Golden Retriever....8
German Shorthaired Pointer....9
Cocker Spaniel....10
English Springer Spaniel....11
Brittany....12
Irish Setter....13
Vizsla....14
Gordon Setter....15
Meet the Hound Dogs....16
Top Dog: Bloodhound....17
Basset Hound....18
Beagle....19
Irish Wolfhound....20
Rhodesian Ridgeback....21
Dachshund....22
Afghan Hound....23
Meet the Working Dogs....24
Top Dog: Boxer....25
Siberian Husky....26
Bernese Mountain Dog....27
Rottweiler....28
Akita....29
Great Dane....30
Mastiff....31
Meet the Terrier Dogs....32
Top Dog: Miniature Schnauzer....33
West Highland White Terrier....34
Airedale Terrier....35
Cairn Terrier....36
Scottish Terrier....37
Bull Terrier....38
Staffordshire Bull Terrier....39
Meet the Toy Dogs....40
Top Dog: Pekingese....41
Pomeranian....42
Chihuahua....43
Yorkshire Terrier....44
Shih Tzu....45
Meet the Herding Dogs....46
Top Dog: Border Collie....47
Australian Shepherd....48
Old English Sheepdog....49
Rough Collie....50
German Shepherd....51
Pembroke Welsh Corgi....52
Bearded Collie....53
Meet the Non-Sporting Dogs....54
Top Dog: Poodle....55
Boston Terrier....56
Bulldog....57
Chow Chow....58
Chinese Shar-Pei....59
Dalmatian....60
American Eskimo....61
Finnish Spitz....62
Lhasa Apso....63
Furever Lovable....64

A Friendship in Dog Years

Dogs are probably humankind's best friend. They began a long time ago as our protectors, helpers, and companions. We later bred dogs for specific jobs or traits. But over time, they wagged and wiggled their way into our hearts.

Of the more than 340 breeds found today, some still do jobs, but their most important job is to love and be loved. And let's talk about those puppy eyes. Science shows dogs have mastered them to make us love them more—as if that's possible!

Achieving Pupfection

A newborn puppy often looks very different from the dog it will become. When it is born, a puppy can't see, hear, or walk. But it grows up quickly! Between eight and twelve weeks old, the puppy is ready to move from its dog pack to a human pack. By the time most dogs are a year old, they are fully grown and are considered adults.

Research shows development of a one-year-old dog is compared to a thirty-year-old human. Then, aging slows down from there! A twelve-year-old large breed is about seventy human years old.

Meet the Sporting Dogs

These dogs were bred for high-energy activity, so be prepared to give your sporting breed lots of outdoor exercise!

TOP DOG

Labrador Retriever

This happy-go-lucky dog wins paws-down as the most popular sporting breed in the United States and England. It is great at retrieving prey, but it is equally at home with its family. This dog loves long walks—on which it loves to meet new friends—and swimming. It especially enjoys playing fetch in the water.

Breed at a Glance:

Height: 21.5–24.5 in. (54.6–62.2 cm)
Weight: 55–80 lbs. (25–36.3 kg)
Coat: Short outercoat with weather-resistant undercoat
Colors: Yellow, black, or chocolate
In a word: People-pleaser

Golden Retriever

The popular golden retriever is similar in size to a Lab but with a long, golden coat. This smart, fun-loving dog is especially good at reading the needs of its people. It's as easy to please as it is to train, and it makes an eager walking or running companion. Happiness is wherever its people are—especially if water is nearby!

Breed at a Glance:

Height: 21.5–24 in. (54.6–60.1 cm)
Weight: 55–75 lbs. (24.9–34 kg)
Coat: Medium
Colors: Varied shades of gold or cream
In a word: Playful

German Shorthaired Pointer

This dog was bred to point, retrieve, and track. And one thing you might have noticed by now about working dogs is they need to be kept busy. It loves going anywhere—on a run, to a park, to a game or other event—as long as it's with its people. This peppy pointer is an ideal agility or fly ball dog, and it is a good candidate for competitive obedience training.

Paw Prints Throughout History

The US Air Force and the Transportation Security Administration use German shorthaired pointers to sniff out bombs.

Breed at a Glance:

Height: 17.5–20.5 in. (44.5–52 cm)
Weight: 30–45 lbs. (13.6–20.4 kg)
Coat: Thick and wavy
Colors: Varied
In a word: Fun-loving

Cocker Spaniel

With its sweet, gentle but playful disposition, the cocker spaniel long held the No. 1 spot among US dog lovers. The smallest of all sporting breeds, this dog was bred to hunt, but it has won its place as a favorite family companion. It enjoys joining family activities, but it is equally content sitting on a lap. Despite its long coat, it doesn't shed much—good news if you're on vacuum duty!

PAW PRINTS THROUGHOUT HISTORY

A cocker spaniel became one of the first European settlers in the United States when it came over on the *Mayflower* in 1620.

BREED AT A GLANCE:

Height: 13.5–15.5 in (34.3–38.1 cm)
Weight: 15–30 lbs. (6.8–13.6 kg)
Coat: Double-coated with long, silky outercoat
Colors: Varied
In a word: Cuddly

English Springer Spaniel

This dog needs its people as much, if not more, than its people need it. Like its cousin the cocker, this spaniel is loving, playful, and easy to train. It's also smart and versatile. It can go from being a family pet by week to a hunting dog by weekend. If used just as a family dog, be sure to give the springer plenty of daily exercise.

Breed at a Glance:

Height: 19–20 in. (48.3–50.8 cm)
Weight: 40–50 lbs. (18.1–22.7 kg)
Coat: Double-coated with weather-resistant outercoat
Colors: Black and white, liver and white, tricolor
In a word: Family-friendly

Brittany

With its roots in France, the American Brittany was bred to run and hunt, making it a good fit for an active family. It especially loves trips to the park, where it will likely track scents and point at potential prey. But even at its most focused, it still listens closely to the voice of its owner. With training, a Brittany can become a winning show, obedience, or agility dog.

Breed at a Glance:

Height: 17.5–20.5 in. (44.5–52 cm)
Weight: 30–45 lbs. (13.6–20.4 kg)
Coat: Thick and wavy
Colors: Varied
In a word: Fun-loving

Irish Setter

This setter is more than just beautiful. It's also easygoing, fun-loving, active, and friendly to everyone it meets. If it were a person, it would be the class clown—because this smart pup enjoys its mischief. It also enjoys chewing, digging, and barking, so training is a must. Lots of exercise helps it remain physically and mentally healthy, and lots of brushing keeps it at its head-turning best.

Breed at a Glance:

Height: 21.5–27 in. (54.6–68.6 cm)
Weight: 60–75 lbs. (27.2–34 kg)
Coat: Medium long
Colors: Chestnut red, sometimes with white markings
In a word: Goofball

Paw Prints Throughout History

The White House has had an occasional red streak within it. Presidents Harry Truman, Richard Nixon, and Ronald Reagan all owned Irish setters during their terms.

Vizsla

Once the prized pet of nobility, the vizsla has since become an all-around popular pet. This friendly, energetic, smart family dog is perfect for active lifestyles. Pay attention to the word "active." This dog needs a lot of activity to keep it from getting into trouble out of boredom. It loves running and hiking. Its outgoing nature makes the vizsla a great therapy dog.

Paw Prints Throughout History

An ancient breed, the vizsla almost went extinct in the late 19th century. Fortunately, the breed rebounded—and keeps bounding today!

Breed at a Glance:

Height: 21–25 in. (53.3–63.5 cm)
Weight: 44–66 lbs. (20–30 kg)
Coat: Short and thick
Color: Rusty red
In a word: People-centered

Gordon Setter

The largest of the setters, the Gordon setter is a combination family dog and watchdog. It loves its people but also is wary of strangers. This high-energy pup enjoys exercising outdoors in any weather. Of course, all those walks in the woods or trips to its favorite swimming hole will mean a lot of brushing for this long-haired beauty. But we suspect it will be a labor of love.

Breed at a Glance:

Height: 23–27 in. (58.4–68.6 cm)
Weight: 45–80 lbs. (20.4–36.3 kg)
Coat: Long and silky
Colors: Black with tan
In a word: Happy-go-lucky

Meet the Hound Dogs

Hound dogs come in all sizes and shapes, but they're all known for their superpowered sniffers and their unique baying sound, a mix of a bark and a howl.

TOP DOG

Bloodhound

Known for its keen nose, the bloodhound is the No. 1 search-and-rescue dog in the world. But this drooling, lovable hound is also a great family dog. It loves walks, especially in parks where it can put its nose to good use. And it really loves its people. This dog doesn't like to be left alone. But when you look into those sad, deep-set eyes, how could you leave it behind?

Breed at a Glance:

Height: 23–27 in. (58.4–68.6 cm)
Weight: About 80–119 lbs. (36.3–54 kg)
Coat: Short and weatherproof
Colors: Black and tan or liver and tan
In a word: Easygoing

Basset Hound

Only the bloodhound has a better sense of smell than the basset hound, which has also become a family favorite. It is loyal and gentle, and it doesn't require a lot of activity. The long, floppy ears demand petting, and the soulful eyes will make you want to meet this dog's every whim. But be warned: This stubborn pup may win in a battle of wills.

Breed at a Glance:

Height: Up to 15 in. (38.1 cm)
Weight: 40–65 lbs. (18.1–29.5 kg)
Coat: Short
Colors: Varied, but usually tricolor
In a word: Devoted

Beagle

Bred to be a pack dog, the lovable beagle enjoys being close to its family. It's always ready for an adventure, whether that means a trip to the park or a walk in the neighborhood. Wherever it goes, it takes in all the smells, and it never meets a stranger. Its wagging tail gives it a near-constant case of the butt wiggles. Oh, and don't interrupt nap time.

PAW PRINTS THROUGHOUT HISTORY

Early beagles were called pocket beagles because they easily fit into hunters' pockets.

BREED AT A GLANCE:

Height: 13–15 in. (33–38 cm)
Weight: 20–35 lbs. (9.1–15.9 kg)
Coat: Short, thick, and weatherproof
Colors: Usually black, tan, and white
In a word: Friendly

Irish Wolfhound

The tallest of all dog breeds, this hound was bred to serve in wars, as a guard dog, and as a hunter. But the wolfhound is also loving, patient, and loyal to its family. Just when you think this somewhat clumsy dog couldn't grow any more, it keeps growing. And be warned: Those long legs make it easy for this fast-running hound to outpace you!

LOOK AT THE SIZE OF THIS IRISH WOLFHOUND COMPARED TO A CHIHUAHUA!

BREED AT A GLANCE:

Height: 30–34 in. (76.2–86.4 cm)
Weight: 105–more than 120 lbs. (47.6–54.4 kg)
Coat: Medium length and wiry
Colors: Varied
In a word: HUGE

Rhodesian Ridgeback

This hound is easy to spot by the namesake ridge running down its back. Fearless and athletic, this popular pup was bred to hunt lions, and it still makes a great hunting companion. But it also is a loyal and protective family pet. It doesn't like to roughhouse, but it requires a lot of exercise and play to keep it from getting into trouble.

Breed at a Glance:

Height: 24–27 in. (60.1–68.6 cm)
Weight: 70–85 lbs. (31.8–38.6 kg)
Coat: Short and thick
Colors: Tan to reddish tan
In a word: Driven

Paw Prints Throughout History

Once a lion hunter, the Rhodesian ridgeback is a combination of a native African breed mixed with mastiffs, bloodhounds, Great Danes, and greyhounds.

Dachshund

The dachshund is nicknamed "wiener dog" because of its hot-dog-shaped body. Its winning temperament makes it a hot dog among pet lovers. Though little, it loves big and is protective. This tiny pooch is patient, charming, active, and sensitive to its owners' needs. The dachshund is a versatile people-pleaser. It loves to dig and run outside, but it can live happily in a big-city apartment.

Breed at a Glance:

Height: 14–18 in. (35.6–81.3 cm)
Weight: 16–32 lbs. (7.3–14.5 kg)
Coat: Short and thick to wiry or long
Colors: Varied
In a word: Bold

Afghan Hound

The Afghan may be the most beautiful athlete you'll ever see. It loves to run, and it needs lots of exercise and play to keep it healthy and entertained. This loving and faithful family dog is best suited to a household that doesn't have small pets. Be ready: Its long coat requires lots of brushing. But that flying fur is worth the fuss when you see your hound run!

PAW PRINTS THROUGHOUT HISTORY

Legend has it that the Afghan hound, which can keep pace with a racehorse, was among the animals preserved on Noah's ark.

BREED AT A GLANCE:

Height: 25–27 in. (63.5–68.6 cm)
Weight: 50–60 lbs. (22.7–27.2 kg)
Coat: Long and silky
Colors: Varied
In a word: Diva

Meet the

Working Dogs

Bred to do specific jobs, these intelligent, strong dogs make alert watchdogs and faithful family companions.

TOP DOG

Boxer

The beloved boxer got its name for the way it holds its front paws up like boxing gloves and appears to fight when playing with another dog. But this working breed is more of a lover than a fighter. It loves and protects its family, though it is slow to trust strangers. The boxer requires a lot of exercise, and it loves to play catch or do agility exercises.

Breed at a Glance:

Height: 21–25 in. (53.3–63.5 cm)
Weight: 55–80 lbs. (24.9–36.3 kg)
Coat: Short and shiny
Colors: Tan, sometimes with white markings and black mask
In a word: Playtime!

Siberian Husky

With its wolflike appearance, the husky is the ultimate pack dog, so it's happy to become part of a human pack. It's still used on sled dog teams in snowy areas where roads are few. Its friendly, playful, and sometimes silly temperament has earned it fans all over the world. This silly pooch is prone to frequent cases of the "zoomies" that send it running all around the house.

Breed at a Glance:

Height: 21–23.5 in. (53.3–59.7 cm)
Weight: 35–60 lbs. (15.9–27.2 kg)
Coat: Double-coated with soft outercoat and thick undercoat
Colors: Varied
In a word: Mush!

Paw Prints Throughout History

In 1925, a Siberian husky led a sled dog team to deliver medicine to treat a deadly disease in a remote Alaskan town, saving the people of Nome.

Bernese Mountain Dog

This easygoing giant lives to make its people happy. It is quick to train, gentle, friendly, and loving. It sometimes behaves like a puppy well into adulthood, and what a big puppy it is! The Bernese mountain dog is bred to endure cold weather. Because of its heavy double coat, this fur ball can take a long time to dry off after a bath or swim.

Breed at a Glance:

Height: 23–27.5 in. (58.4–70 cm)
Weight: 80–115 lbs. (36.3–52.2 kg)
Coat: Double-coated, thick, and long
Colors: Tricolor (black, white, and rust)
In a word: Chill

Rottweiler

This powerful protector was bred to travel along long, dangerous paths to transport herds or goods. Rottweilers continue to have protective instincts, especially for family members. The police and the military have long worked with the rottweiler, but it can also be perfectly happy in the lap of its owner. However, it's hard to say how happy the owner will be under the weight of such a large pup!

Breed at a Glance:

Height: 22–27 in. (55.9–68.6 cm)
Weight: 95–135 lbs. (43.1–61.2 kg)
Coat: Medium-length and double-coated
Colors: Black with reddish markings
In a word: Protective

Akita

This large dog is easily identified by its broad head and curly tail. A stubborn dog that likes to do things on its own terms, the Akita is intelligent and strong-willed. It thrives with patient training and loving care. Around family, it is affectionate and playful, but to strangers, the Akita is a protector. It will defend its family, if needed. It does best as an only pet.

Breed at a Glance:

Height: 19–20 in. (48.3–50.8 cm)
Weight: 40–50 lbs. (18.1–22.7 kg)
Coat: Double-coated with weather-resistant outercoat
Colors: Black and white, liver and white, tricolor
In a word: Family-friendly

Paw Prints Throughout History

After Hachikō's original owner died in 1925, he was adopted by another family. However, he kept going to his late owner's home and waited daily at the train station for him for the rest of his life. Talk about loyal!

Great Dane

This impressive pup puts other dogs in its shadow. When it stands on its hind feet, it's often taller than the people around it. Despite its size, the Great Dane is a big softie. It loves kids and family time. It needs lots of walks, but once back at home, it's ready to snuggle. It also is a good watchdog, and its size alone is enough to scare intruders.

PAW PRINTS THROUGHOUT HISTORY

Despite its name, the Great Dane isn't the tiniest bit Danish. It's German. In the 19th century, it was named Germany's national dog.

BREED AT A GLANCE:

Height: 28–32 in. (71.1–81.3 cm)
Weight: 100–175 lb. (45.4–79.4 kg)
Coat: Short and shiny
Colors: Varied
In a word: Giant

Mastiff

The massive mastiff may seem a little scary when you first see it. But with training, it makes a good family dog. It loves and protects its people, and it gets along well with other pets with which it has been raised. Be careful not to give it too much exercise, but be prepared to give it a lot of food. Patient and calm, the mastiff makes a great therapy dog.

Breed at a Glance:

Height: 27.5 in. (69.9 cm) and taller
Weight: 160–230 lbs. (72.6–104.3 kg)
Coat: Double-coated with short outercoat
Colors: Varied
In a word: Woah!

Meet the

Terrier Dogs

Terriers are mostly small in size but big in attitude, heart, and energy. They can make wonderful family companions.

Miniature Schnauzer

This pint-sized pup is popular for a reason: Friendly and affectionate, it insists on being treated like a member of the family. It loves children and other pets, and it is just as suited to farm life as city life. Just don't forget to give it plenty of play breaks and walks, and be aware the mini schnauzer has a serious appetite that has to be kept in check.

Breed at a Glance:

Height: 12–14 in. (30.5–35.6 cm)
Weight: 9–17.5 lbs. (4.1–7.9 kg)
Coat: Wiry outercoat with soft undercoat
Colors: White and black, black and silver, or black
In a word: Alert

West Highland White Terrier

This terrier's cuteness factor and charm are off the charts. It is smart, stubborn, feisty, and active. As adorable as it is, you may not mind it barking excitedly or digging up your yard. It loves to run and chase things, and it is well-suited to dog sports. This tiny little handful of fluff does best in a household with no other pets and plenty of training.

Paw Prints Throughout History

The trademark white coat of the cuddly Westie would help hunters easily spot it in a field.

Breed at a Glance:

Height: 10–11 in. (25.4–27.9 cm)
Weight: 15–22 lbs. (6.8–10 kg)
Coat: Double-coated with rough outercoat
Color: White
In a word: Strong-willed

Airedale Terrier

The Airedale was bred to be smart and brave, and it seems to know it. As a result, it can look and act like a bit of a hotshot. It can be unfriendly to strangers, both human and canine. But to its family, it's gentle, loving, and protective. This pup is always ready for playtime, loves to dig, and enjoys having plenty of chew toys.

BREED AT A GLANCE:

Height: 23 in. (58.4 cm)
Weight: 50–70 lbs. (22.7–31.8 kg)
Coat: Double-coated with wiry outercoat
Colors: Black with tan or mixed with tan
In a word: Proud

Cairn Terrier

Imagine a smile wrapped in fur, and you have a cairn terrier. This dog loves life, people, and snuggles. An active and curious breed, it requires multiple walks each day, and it would enjoy digging up a flower bed or two. It also enjoys chasing small animals like squirrels, rabbits, and chipmunks. With some patient training, a cairn terrier could be a perfect friend for any child.

PAW PRINTS THROUGHOUT HISTORY

The world's most famous cairn terrier was Terry, more popularly known as Toto, the dog star of *The Wizard of Oz*.

BREED AT A GLANCE:

Height: 9.5–10 in. (24.1–25.4 cm)
Weight: 13–14 lbs. (5.9–6.4 kg)
Coat: Weather-resistant double coat
Colors: Varied
In a word: Determined

Scottish Terrier

The Scottie begins life as a playful pup and then gets down to business as an adult. It's bred to work, and it takes that calling seriously. Squeak toys become prey, playing ball becomes an exercise in hunting, and long walks become safety patrols. Devotion to its family also falls under its job description—strangers, not so much. And don't even try to get it to be nice to neighborhood pets.

Breed at a Glance:

Height: 10 in. (25.4 cm)
Weight: 18–22 lbs. (8.2–10 kg)
Coat: Weather-resistant double coat
Colors: Varied
In a word: Feisty

Bull Terrier

Want to play? Want to run? Want to play and run some more? That's the attitude of the forever-playful bull terrier. This dog needs a lot of activity (think games!) to keep it busy and healthy. You'll notice right away that this fun-loving dog likes to play rough! As much as it loves playing, it may love its family more. It is devoted to its people almost to a fault.

Paw Prints Throughout History

The bull terrier can easily be spotted by its egg-shaped face and its unique triangular eyes.

Breed at a Glance:

Height: 21–22 in. (53.3–55.9 cm)
Weight: 50–70 lbs. (22.7–31.8 kg)
Coat: Short and rough
Colors: All white or multicolored
In a word: Silly

Staffordshire Bull Terrier

If Mary Poppins were a dog, she would be a Staffordshire bull terrier, nicknamed a "nanny dog" because of how much it loves and protects children. Once bred for fighting, the modern Staffy is a smart, gentle, loyal family dog. Be prepared to take this playful pooch for lots of long walks, and allow it to run often in a fenced area. And make sure it has plenty of friends.

Breed at a Glance:

Height: 14–16 in. (35.6–40.6 cm)
Weight: 24–38 lbs. (10.9–17.2 kg)
Coat: Short and smooth
Colors: Varied
In a word: Sweet

Meet the Toy Dogs

There's room in this world—plenty of room, in fact!—for the tiny bundles of love found among the toy breeds that exist just to be adored and enjoyed.

TOP DOG

Pekingese

In ancient China, you could be punished by death for stealing a Pekingese, a favorite dog among rulers. This charming little fluff ball appears to be smiling all the time. It bonds closely with one person, so it's not ideal for a family. Because it isn't too crazy about other pets, playdates are a must to help it become more friendly. This dog likes to play and get pampered.

Breed at a Glance:

Height: 6–9 in. (15.2–22.9 cm)
Weight: 8–14 lbs. (3.6–6.4 kg)
Coat: Long outercoat with thick undercoat
Colors: Varied
In a word: Devoted

Pomeranian

A big dog trapped in a small dog's body, the Pomeranian sees itself as the boss of everything and everyone. It loves to be at the center of all family activities, and it is always in danger of getting spoiled. This active breed loves to walk, walk, and walk some more, and then play, play, and play some more. And did someone say "car ride?"

Breed at a Glance:

Height: About 7 in. (17.8 cm)
Weight: 3–7 lbs. (1.4–3.2 kg)
Coat: Double-coated with long, straight outercoat
Colors: Varied, either solid or mixed
In a word: Curious

Chihuahua

Among the world's most popular dogs, the Chihuahua has more personality than its tiny frame can contain. It is confident—even a little too confident. The petite pooch wants to be with its people all the time, and it will happily let itself be carried around inside a bag or dog carrier. This often pampered pet is known to be picky. And no loud noises or rough play, please!

Paw Prints Throughout History

This micro pup—which has been bred to become smaller over time—is named for Chihuahua, Mexico, where it originated.

Breed at a Glance:

Height: 5–8 in. (12.7–20.3 cm)
Weight: Up to 6 lbs. (2.7 kg)
Coat: Double-coated or single-coated, short or long
Colors: Varied
In a word: Attitude

Yorkshire Terrier

Don't try to tell the Yorkie it's too small to do anything. Its confidence and personality make up for its small size. Brave and spirited, it makes a good watchdog, and it can be a source of laughter for years to come. Its trademark coat requires a lot of brushing and never stops growing. But in good news, it doesn't shed. This portable pup makes a good apartment or city dog.

Breed at a Glance:

Height: 7–8 in. (17.8–20.3 cm)
Weight: 7 lbs. (3.2 kg)
Coat: Famously long
Colors: Varied
In a word: Pup-ular

Shih Tzu

If you're looking for a lovable lap dog, the easy-to-spoil shih tzu is the dog for you. This perky powder puff is sweet, loving, and gentle toward everyone. It loves play breaks, but it doesn't need much more than a short walk each day to keep it happy and healthy. Pamper this pooch with lots of daily brushing and weekly baths, but beware of giving it too many treats!

PAW PRINTS THROUGHOUT HISTORY

The shih tzu's name means "little lion." According to legend, the tiny pup could change into a huge lion.

BREED AT A GLANCE:

Height: 9–10.5 in. (22.9–26.7 cm)
Weight: 9–16 lbs. (4.1–7.3 kg)
Coat: Double-coated with long, silky outercoat
Colors: Varied
In a word: Spunky

Meet the Herding Dogs

Herders are at the head of their class in intelligence! Be ready to give them lots of physical and mental exercise to keep them busy.

TOP DOG

Border Collie

The energetic border collie is the world's No. 1 most intelligent breed—about as smart as a human toddler. This friendly pup needs lots of exercise, playtime, and training. In herding fashion, it will nip at hands or feet of its animal or human "herd" without hurting. But with training, little is impossible for the border collie, which excels in agility. It is a loyal companion for an active family.

Breed at a Glance:

Height: 19–22 in. (48.3–55.9 cm)
Weight: 30–50 lbs. (13.6–22.7 kg)
Coat: Medium to long
Colors: Varied
In a word: Smart

Australian Shepherd

Known for its beautiful coat and eyes, this bobtailed canine is smart, friendly, and obedient. It loves making people happy, and it can be an ideal therapy dog. The Aussie's high energy level demands it have plenty of room to run. A farm or ranch is perfect for this herder, but a large yard will do. It loves kids and playtime, and it's protective of its human herd.

Breed at a Glance:

Height: 18–23 in. (45.7–58.4 cm)
Weight: 40–65 lbs. (18.1–29.5 kg)
Coat: Weather-resistant double coat with medium-length outercoat
Colors: Varied
In a word: Eager

Old English Sheepdog

Perky and kind, this woolly heart-warmer returns love with love. It was bred to herd cattle, and it will bump kids in its family in an attempt to herd them. Though it loves and needs exercise, including runs in fenced areas, this large breed can adapt to apartment or city life with enough time outdoors. Winter is its favorite season, so set aside time on snowy days for outdoor playtime.

PAW PRINTS THROUGHOUT HISTORY

The Old English sheepdog's name is a little deceiving. Despite its name, it's a fairly new breed, and it's not really a sheep herder.

BREED AT A GLANCE:

Height: 21–24 in. (53.3–61 cm)
Weight: 60–100 lbs. (27.2–45.4 kg)
Coat: Shaggy, weatherproof double coat
Colors: White with a variety of other colors
In a word: Patient

Rough Collie

It's hard not to want to hug a friendly, fluffy collie. And if you're not won over by this dog's looks, you'll be won over by its heart and intelligence. It is sensitive, easy to train, and brave, sometimes putting itself in danger to protect its family. Like other herders, it needs plenty of walks and opportunities to run—and maybe even a visit to a local sheep or goat farm.

Paw Prints Throughout History

The most famous rough collie of all is Lassie of TV and movie fame. Nine males played Lassie over the years of the canine icon's stardom.

Breed at a Glance:

Height: 22–26 in. (55.9–66 cm)
Weight: 50–75 lbs. (19.7–29.5 kg)
Coat: Double-coated with long outercoat
Colors: Varied
In a word: Legendary

German Shepherd

The German shepherd is the world's No. 1 service dog with the police, the military, or as a guard dog—and for many good reasons. This imposing dog is brave, loyal, intelligent, eager to please, and easy to train. Yet it's patient with children and sensitive to the needs of those around it. The more time you spend with a German shepherd, the more convinced you'll be that there's nothing it can't do.

BREED AT A GLANCE:

Height: 22–26 in. (55.9–66 cm)
Weight: 65–90 lbs. (29.5–40.8 kg)
Coat: Medium-length double coat
Colors: Black, tan, or reddish
In a word: BOSS

Pembroke Welsh Corgi

This low-to-the-ground breed is big on personality and confidence. And do you know what else is big about it? Its bark! Family is everything to this tiny watchdog, and it can bark a lot if excited—which may be often—or if it thinks a stranger poses a threat to its herd. It is as playful as it is bold and as happy as it is stubborn.

PAW PRINTS THROUGHOUT HISTORY

The Pembroke Welsh corgi came to us from fairies or Vikings, depending upon which legend you believe. Even if the corgi isn't enchanted, you will find it enchanting.

BREED AT A GLANCE:

Height: 10–12 in. (25.4–30.5 cm)
Weight: 20–30 lbs. (9.1–13.6 kg)
Coat: Double-coated with short outercoat
Colors: Varied
In a word: Adorable

Bearded Collie

At first glance, you may mistake this shaggy pooch for an Old English sheepdog, though this collie is more lean and has a tail. Named for its beard, this playful pup happily bounces and barks through its day. It promises to bring smiles and laughter to any active family. Wet or cold weather is welcomed by this dog, which loves long walks and occasional runs in large fenced areas.

Breed at a Glance:

Height: 20–22 in. (50.8–55.9 cm)
Weight: 45–55 lbs. (17.7–21.7 kg)
Coat: Shaggy and double-coated
Colors: Varied
In a word: Bouncy

Meet the Non-Sporting Dogs

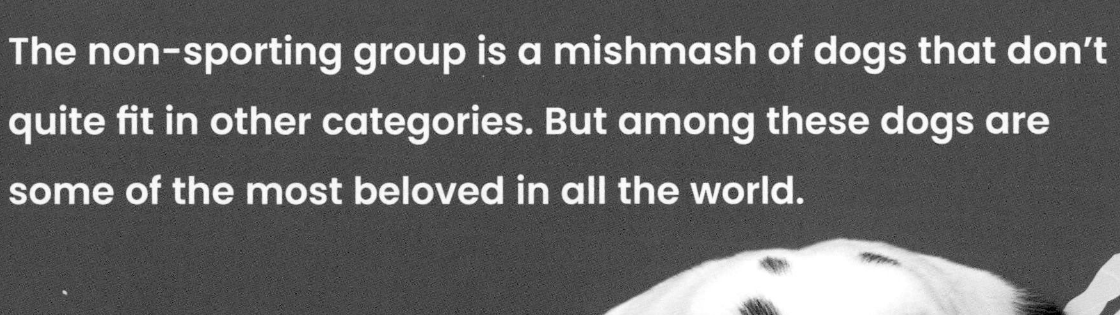

The non-sporting group is a mishmash of dogs that don't quite fit in other categories. But among these dogs are some of the most beloved in all the world.

Poodle

The poodle—with its wide range of sizes—is one of the most popular dog breeds. Stylish and smart, this puffy pooch isn't too dignified to enjoy a romp in the water or a game of fetch outside. You won't find a prettier or more willing walking or jogging companion. A poodle's hair (yes, hair and not fur) must be maintained. Even at its prettiest, the poodle needs lots of activity.

Breed at a Glance:

Height: No more than 10 in. (25.4 cm) for toy–23.5 in. (59.7 cm) for standard
Weight: Up to 8 lbs. (3.6 kg) for toy–70 lbs. (31.8 kg) for standard
Coat: Medium and woolly
Colors: Varied
In a word: Fancy

Boston Terrier

This tuxedoed terrier brings its "A" game to each and every day. Playful to the point of being silly, it's a source of fun and laughter in any home. It loves its people and is an excellent companion on outings. City life suits the Boston, which is never short on friends. If you choose to sleep with your Boston, you may want to wear earplugs. It snores!

Breed at a Glance:

Height: 15–17 in. (38.1–43.2 cm)
Weight: 12–25 lbs. (5.4–11.3 kg)
Coat: Short and smooth
Colors: White with black, mottled colors, or reddish black
In a word: Partier

Paw Prints Throughout History

Boston terriers have become well known for—wait for it—their farts. They're adorable, tiny fart factories.

Bulldog

Don't let that face fool you. This dog is gentle, loving, and friendly to all. It lives to bring joy to those around it, making it easy to train. It naturally makes a good watchdog, for which it likes to be repaid with cuddles and attention. The bulldog can't take too much exercise, but be sure to keep it stocked with plenty of chew toys.

Breed at a Glance:

Height: 13–15 in. (33–38.1 cm)
Weight: 40–50 lbs. (18.1–22.7 kg)
Coat: Short
Colors: Varied
In a word: Charmer

Chow Chow

A clean freak with no doggy odor, a chow chow is the ideal pet for a single person living in an apartment or in the city—if you can train it to control its barking. This protective, strong-willed dog needs to be taught gently and repeatedly who's in charge of its pack. It does well with daily walks, and it is fairly low-maintenance aside from regular brushing.

Breed at a Glance:

Height: 17–22 in. (43.2–55.9 cm)
Weight: 45–70 lbs. (20.4–31.8 kg)
Coat: Double-coated with medium outercoat
Colors: Varied
In a word: Protective

Chinese Shar-Pei

As a longtime guardian of livestock, this wrinkly-crinkly pooch will protect and defend its beloved family. Family is everything to this dog, which doesn't take well to strangers. The shar-pei is both smart and stubborn, but persistent training pays off. This pet will reward its family with love and affection. A low-energy breed, this pooch doesn't need much exercise, and it takes well to pampering.

BREED AT A GLANCE:

Height: 18–20 in. (45.7–50.8 cm)
Weight: 45–60 lbs. (20.4–22.7 kg)
Coat: Short and bristly
Colors: Varied solid colors
In a word: Wrinkly

PAW PRINTS THROUGHOUT HISTORY

The ancient Chinese had a purpose for breeding the shar-pei to have all those adorable wrinkles. The wrinkles protect its organs from injury if another dog bites it.

Dalmatian

Long the mascot of the local fire station, the dalmatian is smart, energetic, and always ready to go. It especially loves jogging and hiking. The active dalmatian does best in a home with a fenced yard. Sometimes its curiosity gets it into trouble. This breed—made famous in the movie *101 Dalmatians*—needs to be kept stocked with plenty of chew toys. A very devoted dog, it may pout when left alone.

Paw Prints Throughout History

Dalmatians once ran ahead of fire trucks to warn people to get out of the way of oncoming firefighters.

Breed at a Glance:

Height: 19–24 in. (48.3–60.1 cm)
Weight: 45–70 lbs. (20.4–31.8 kg)
Coat: Short
Colors: White with black or brown spots
In a word: Spots!

American Eskimo

You may not be able to resist hugging an Eskie, and that's totally okay. This loving pup is all about snuggles. It loves its people to a fault, and it doesn't like to be left alone. It is an alert watchdog with a warning bark. Active and intelligent, the eager-to-please Eskie requires lots of exercise and playtime. Just be careful not to lose it in a snowdrift!

Breed at a Glance:

Height: 9 in. (22.9 cm) for toy–19 in. (48.3 cm) for standard
Weight: 6 lbs. (2.7 kg) for toy–35 lbs. (15.9 kg) for standard
Coat: Fluffy and double-coated
Colors: White or white and cream
In a word: Fluffy

Finnish Spitz

If you need someone to talk to, the Finnish spitz is more than willing to fill the bill. One of the most vocal dog breeds, the spitz barks at strangers—and a lot of other things. In fact, the spitz happily competes in barking contests in its homeland of Finland. This breed is bred for colder climates and is a heavy shedder. Bring on the snow and the dog brush!

Breed at a Glance:

Height: 15.5–20 in. (39.4–50.8 cm)
Weight: 23–33 lbs. (10.4–15 kg)
Coat: Short outercoat, thick undercoat
Colors: Tan to golden red
In a word: Yodeler

Lhasa Apso

This royal-looking breed believes it has the right to be spoiled. Though loving and playful, this natural watchdog is quick to let its people know what—or who—it likes and doesn't like. A good city or apartment dog, the Lhasa apso doesn't need much exercise, and it's not a fan of rough play. However, it makes for a faithful and enjoyable family companion.

Paw Prints Throughout History

Once treasured among Buddhists in its homeland of Tibet, the Lhasa apso is sometimes used as a service dog for the hearing impaired.

Breed at a Glance:

Height: 10–11 in. (25.4–27.9 cm)
Weight: 12–18 lbs. (5.4–8.2 kg)
Coat: Long outercoat with thick undercoat
Colors: Varied
In a word: Spoil-worthy

Fur-ever Lovable

Dogs began as our protectors and helpers. They have kept us safe, helped us track food, protected our herds and our homes, and guided us on long journeys. But modern dogs are so much more. They live to love and be loved. They make our world a better, happier place. They never judge and are quick to forgive.

And when we curl up with our favorite pup, we truly know we're home. As Charles Schulz of *Peanuts* fame wrote, "Happiness is a warm puppy." Our recommendation: Go find some happiness today.

Highlights Puzzle Readers

LEVEL
LET'S EXPLORE READING

Nick and Nack Blow Bubbles

By Brandon Budzi
Art by Charles Lehman

HIGHLIGHTS PRESS
Honesdale, Pennsylvania

Stories + Puzzles = Reading Success!

Dear Parents,

Highlights Puzzle Readers are an innovative approach to learning to read that combines puzzles and stories to build motivated, confident readers.

Developed in collaboration with reading experts, the stories and puzzles are seamlessly integrated so that readers are encouraged to read the story, solve the puzzles, and then read the story again. This helps increase vocabulary and reading fluency and creates a satisfying reading experience for any kind of learner. In addition, solving Hidden Pictures puzzles fosters important reading and learning skills such as:

- letter and shape recognition
- letter-sound relationships
- visual discrimination
- logic
- flexible thinking
- sequencing

With high-interest stories, humorous characters, and trademark puzzles, Highlights Puzzle Readers offer a winning combination for inspiring young learners to love reading.

This is Nick.

This is Nack.

Nick loves to **make** things.
Nack loves to **find** things.
They make a good **team**.

You can help them by solving the **Hidden Pictures** puzzles.

Happy reading!

Nick and Nack ride their bicycles.

"Watch out for the puddle!" says Nick.

"Oh no!" says Nack.

SPLOOSH!

“Look at our bicycles!” says Nack. “They are dirty.”

“We can wash them,” says Nick.

“Here is soap.”

“Here is water,” says Nack.

Nick and Nack wash their bicycles.

"Look at the bubbles!" says Nick.

"Can we make more bubbles?"

asks Nack.

“Yes!” says Nick.

“We need to make a wand.

Then we can blow more bubbles.”

"What can we use to make a wand?"

asks Nack.

"I need straws," says Nick.

"I will make a big wand.

I want to make big bubbles!"

“I can help find straws,” says Nack.

“I found the straws!” says Nack.

“Now I need to make a circle,” says Nick.

“Can you use string?” asks Nack.

“Yes!” says Nick.

Help Nick and Nack.

Find 5 balls of string hidden in the picture.

"I will make a little wand," says Nack.

"I want to make little bubbles!"

"Do we have pipe cleaners?"

asks Nick.

"I can help find pipe cleaners,"

says Nack.

"I found pipe cleaners!" says Nack.

"You can bend a pipe cleaner
to make a wand," says Nick.

"Can I also add beads?" asks Nack.

"Yes!" says Nick.

Help Nick and Nack.
Find 5 beads hidden in the picture.

"We also need to make bubble mix,"
says Nack.

"We can use soap," says Nick.
"Where did we put the soap?"

"I can help find the soap,"
says Nack.

Nack finds a scarf.

He finds a sign.

He finds a saw.

He cannot find soap.

“Here is the soap!” says Nack.

“We will mix the soap with water,” says Nick.

“We can put the mix in a pail,” says Nack.

Help Nick and Nack.
Find 5 pails hidden in the picture.

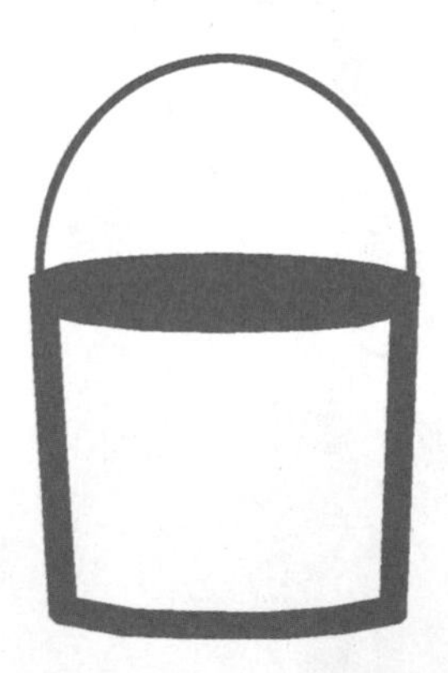

Soap

“First, we can make the wands!” says Nick.

He makes a big wand.

Nack makes a little wand.

“Our wands are done!” says Nick.

“Now we can make the bubble mix.”

Nack fills up the pail with water.

Then Nick adds the soap.

They stir the bubble mix.

"Time to blow bubbles!" says Nick.

“Look!” says Nack.

“I blew a little bubble.”

“Look!” says Nick.

“I blew a big bubble.”

“How can we blow
more bubbles?” asks Nack.

“We can use a fan!” says Nick.

Help Nick and Nack.
Find 5 fans hidden in the picture.

Blow Your Own BUBBLES!

Nick's Bubble Wand

WHAT YOU NEED:

- 2 straws
- String
- Scissors

1 Cut a piece of string six times as long as the length of a straw.

2 Thread the string through the two straws.

3 Tie the ends of the string together. Slide the knot into one of the straws.

4 Hold the straws as handles. Dip the wand and your hands into the bubble mix to create large bubbles.

BUBBLE MIX

WHAT YOU NEED:

- Pail
- 3 cups of "soft" or distilled water
- 6 tablespoons of dish detergent
- 3 tablespoons of glycerin or corn syrup

1. Put the "soft" or distilled water in a clean bucket.
2. Add the dish detergent and glycerin or corn syrup.
3. Gently stir the mixture. Try not to create suds.
4. Let the mixture sit for a few hours or overnight before using.

Nack's Bubble Wand

WHAT YOU NEED:

- Pipe cleaner
- Beads

This wand is a circle, but you can make any shape you want, like a heart or a triangle.

1 Create a loop at the top of a chenille stick. Twist the end of the loop around the handle to hold the loop in place.

2 Add beads onto the end of the chenille stick.

3 Tuck the end of the pipe cleaner into the bottom bead. Have fun blowing small bubbles!

Nick and Nack's TIPS

- Gather your supplies before you start crafting.
- Ask an adult or robot for help with anything sharp or hot.
- Clean up your workspace when your craft is done.

For information about permission to reprint selections from this book, please contact permissions@highlights.com.

Published by Highlights Press
815 Church Street
Honesdale, Pennsylvania 18431
ISBN (paperback): 978-1-64472-194-0
ISBN (hardcover): 978-1-64472-195-7
ISBN (ebook): 978-1-64472-239-8

Library of Congress Control Number: 2020949551
Printed in Melrose Park, IL, USA
Mfg. 03/2021
First edition
Visit our website at Highlights.com.
10 9 8 7 6 5 4 3 2 1

Craft instructions by Elizabeth Wyrsch-Ba
Craft samples by Lisa Glover
Photos by Jim Filipski, Guy Cali Associates, Inc.

This book has been officially leveled by using the F&P Text Level Gradient™ Leveling System.

For assistance in the preparation of this book, the editors would like to thank Vanessa Maldonado, MSEd, MS Literacy Ed. K–12, Reading/LA Consultant Cert., K–5 Literacy Instructional Coach; and Gina Shaw.